70 YEARS OF THE BEANO

The fact that The Beano has reached its 70th birthday is not sim[...]
history – it is a milestone in BRITISH history, so nationally belov[...]
cartoon characters.

Lord Snooty, Biffo the Bear, General Jumbo, Jonah, Dennis the Menace, Roger the Dodger,
Minnie the Minx, The Bash Street Kids…the names roll off the tongue like some legendary
football team. And legends they are, for there can be very few children, parents or grandparents
in Britain today who are not familiar with the colourful world of The Beano.

But, enough preamble, Beanofans, we're wasting good comic reading time and there are great
moments from seven decades of fun and mayhem just ahead.

Big Eggo

WATCHED over by cute little Peanut, Big Eggo the ostrich fronted The Beano for the first 10 years, on some of the most colourful covers ever produced.

Lord Snooty

IN the early days the top cartoon strip was Lord Snooty, drawn by the talented Dudley D Watkins. Snooty, the young Earl of Bunkerton, was a titled lord of the realm but for fun and true friendship, stole away over his castle wall to play with the ragged urchins on Ash Can Alley.

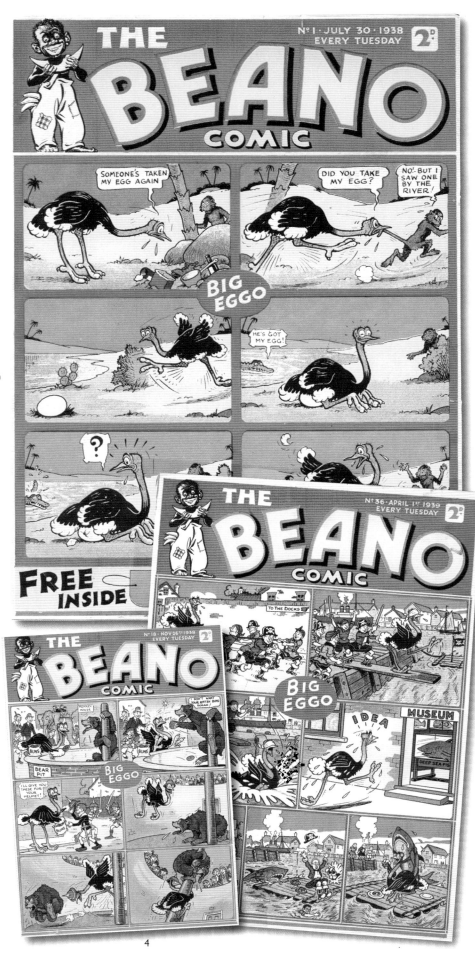

LORD SNOOTY AND HIS PALS

A lot of early Beano funnies were small, single gag strips, arranged three to a page. This format produced a busy layout which continued into the early 50s.

WEE PEEM
THE TEACHER SCOWLS, WHEN PUSSY HOWLS!

LITTLE DEAD EYE DICK
HE PLAYS A JAPE— AND CHANGES SHAPE

HAIRY DAN
DAN MAKES A COPPER COME A CROPPER.

MARY'S NOT DENSE — SHE'S GOT HORSE SENSE

THE ELECTRIC TRICK WAS PRETTY SLICK

HELPFUL HENRY
HENRY CHOPS WOOD— BUT IT DOES HIM NO GOOD

MAXY'S TAXI

OUR CABBY'S HERE – WITH FUN AND CHEER!

HAVE-A-GO JOE

DO OR DIE – HE'LL HAVE A TRY!

THE MAGIC LOLLIPOPS

SUCK 'EM AND SEE!

● An early Christmas gift for Beano kids. Was Rolf Harris around then too?

EARLY Beano fans loved a good read so text stories made up a big part of the comic. In the first years 10 out of the 28 pages were full text. Later, as tastes changed, these same adventure stories would be retold in picture form.

THE first series of Pansy Potter was so popular it made her a household name. The Beano strong-arm girl was drawn by three famous artists, Hugh McNeil, Basil Blackaller and Sam Fair. The strip shown here was drawn by Basil Blackaller, aged 19.

● Big Eggo catches a Nazi spy in the wartime cover caper.

● Fascist leaders Hitler and Mussolini are lampooned in this cartoon.

The Beano at War

ILLUSTRATING the great British ability to laugh in the face of adversity, The Beano continued to pour out its fun-filled pages during the dark days of World War 2. However the wonderful jokes and stories were served up with a large helping of patriotism as the comic's characters tackled the Nazis in highly imaginative ways.

BEANO readers were encouraged to save paper for recycling, all in aid of the war effort. Paper shortages had already affected Beano readers, the comic went fortnightly, coming out on alternate weeks to the sister paper The Dandy. The page count had to go down as well, the Beano of April 1942 was reduced to 12 pages and stayed this way for the duration of the war.(Post war, in April 1947, the page count dropped to 10 as shortages bit hard.)

COME ON GIRLS! COME ON CHAPS! DOT HITLER ON THE NAPPER. SAVE UP ALL YOUR LITTLE SCRAPS, AND BE A "PAPER SCRAPPER"!

— Don't make paper aeroplanes with your old comics —
— Help to make REAL ONES →
SAVE WASTE PAPER

Adolf started off this caper
But soon we'll stop his caper
If every British boy and girl
Keeps saving up WASTE PAPER!

SALVAGE DUMP

IF HITLER HAD A MAGIC TELESCOPE WOULD HE SEE THIS?
HIMMEL! DER PIG-DOG BRITISH ARE SAVING ALL THEIR WASTE PAPER
WASTE PAPER DEPOT
IT'S UP TO YOU! SPEED OLD HITLER TO HIS GRAVE WITH ALL THE PAPER YOU CAN SAVE!

HOI! SAVE WASTE PAPER!
IT HELPS TO WIN THE WAR!

Lord Snooty's War

L ORD Snooty and his pals were the most patriotic of strips, they set about the enemy in a series of fantastic adventures that ran through the early war years. These two strips are classic examples.

D OCUMENTS found after the war indicated, along with the editors of some national newspapers, the editors of The Beano and Dandy would have been arrested had Hitler's forces invaded Britain.

Casualty of War

THE Magic comic was launched on July 22, 1939 as a third brother to the already super successful Dandy and Beano comics. It was very colourful and aimed at a slightly younger audience. The paper and ink shortages that had forced the Dandy and Beano to go fortnightly hit The Magic worst of all. After only 80 issues, it closed.

FREE INSIDE – SUGAR BULLETS TO EAT

THE MAGIC COMIC

N°1 · 22ⁿ JULY · 1939
EVERY THURSDAY
2ᴰ

Every Thursday · THE MAGIC

SOOTY SN

KOKO THE PUP

FULL OF TRICKS AND FULL OF FUN. KOKO'S A PAL FOR EVERYONE!

Two wanderers, brave as brave can be,
Are in the desert, as you see.
They're Mr Sam Coot and his wife,
And this is how they spend their life.

But now across the sa...
For they've just seen...
As black as a well-pol...
And so they raise thei...

But they won't hurt the little lad,
Says Mr Coot, "Just call me Dad!"
And in their camp they give him lots
Of scrumptious food from tins and pots.

"Just look at him,"
"Why, he's as bla...
Sam, dear, let us s...
Sooty Snowball—wh...

Sooty thinks it's all a dream!
That bowl is filled with yellow cream
That Ned's been whipping all the day—
So greedy Sooty licks away.

Oh, Sooty, Sooty, you're a sow!
Just look and see what's happening now!
The bowl tips up, and, terrified,
The little lad lands—splodge!—inside!

Have missed the boy, the big, black cook,
And when they meet the big, black cook,
They say, "Oh, please, Ned, have a look!"

  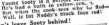

Fat Neddy waddles to the door,
But soon they hear his frightened roar,
"Oh, help me, help!" yells the black gent.
"A turtle's crawling from the tent!"

The Coots come running, full of woe,
While Ned flees, hard as he can go.
But Sam Coot never shirks his duty—
He turns the "turtle"—and finds Sooty!

Young Sooty is a perfect scream,
He's had a bath in yellow cream,
But when the cook sees why he fled—
Well, is fat Neddy's black face red!

When leaving for home the Coots soon find—Next week that they can't leave Sooty behind!

PRINTED AND PUBLISHED IN GREAT BRITAIN BY D. C. THOMSON & CO., LTD., 12 FETTER LANE, FLEET STREET, LONDON, E.C.4.

FOLLOWING the established Dandy/Beano format, The Magic had a very colourful animal cover character and a lead strip inside from the pen of Dudley D Watkins. This was Peter Piper who the story told us, picked people out of pickles by bringing objects to life with his magical pan pipes.

JIMMY AND HIS MAGIC PATCH

AS the war ground on, the patriotic Beano brigade moved towards tales of fantastic adventure absolute escapism for war weary children.

Jimmy and his Magic Patch was exactly such a story – wearing trousers patched with a square from a magic carpet, Jimmy Watson would be whisked off to anywhere or any time in the world, he just had to wish for it.

● He saved Bonnie Prince Charlie in the Scottish highlands

● Jimmy landed in the tomb of the Pharoah

● Fought with King Alfred against the invading Danes

LORD Snooty slowed his bombardment of the Nazis and fell into surreal storylines, many of which ended in fantasy feeds of gigantic proportion. This was the stuff dreams were made of for under-nourished, ration book readers.

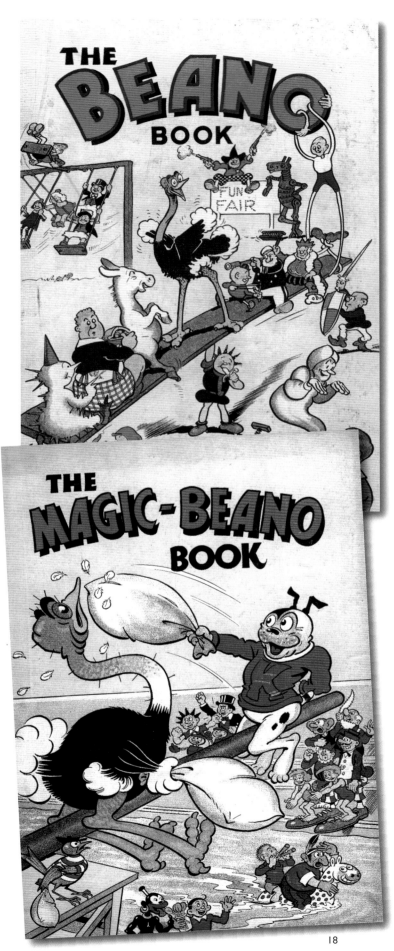

You've read the comic, now read the book...

A YEAR after the weekly had launched, the mighty Beano Book slipped off the stocks, it went on sale September 1939. This is catalogued as the 1940 Beano Book.

The cover featured many characters including the weekly's cover hero, Big Eggo. Many of the book strips did not appear in the weekly, among them Dingo the Doggie, Marmaduke Mean the Miser and Boss and Bert.

I N 1943 the annual became The Magic-Beano Book and incorporated the best strips from the now defunct Magic comic.

Unlike the weekly comic, which contained a strong patriotic message, the book contained only the staple mix of humour, adventure and jokes. Magic was dropped from the title for good in 1950.

A - MUSE - ING !

Said a ragged old beggar called Muse,
" My presence you'll have to excuse.
   My best Sunday coat
   Is in rags, and you'll note
That both soles are quite off my shoes."

THE TIGER WAS TICKLED

There was a bad boy of Pekin
Who tickled a lean tiger's chin.
   The tiger's now fat.
   Can you wonder at that ?
But where is that boy of Pekin ?

125

FREE INSIDE— ADVENTURE FOOTBALL STAMP ALBUM

SEPT. 5TH 1936
No. 775

PRICE TWOPENCE

ADVENTURE

EVERY MONDAY

STRANG THE TERRIBLE

A STRONG feature of the early Beano was a good old ripping yarn – the sort that were the staple of the D.C. Thomson's big 5 boys adventure papers – Rover, Wizard, Skipper, Adventure and Hotspur. One type of yarn stood out, it was the incredible tales of mighty strongmen. Morgyn the Mighty was in The Beano from issue No1.

Morgyn Destroys the Wolves of the Sea!

MORGYN THE MIGHTY

What's the finest comic out?—"The Beano" Comic without doubt.

NEXT TUESDAY—A GHOST SHIP COMES TO BLACK ISLAND!

Another of the muscle men to appear was Samson the Strongman, head of the Shipwreck Circus crew. Throughout its long run the series had a fascination with giant creatures as this advert for The Beano annual shows. Originally drawn by Dudley Watkins.

Strang the Terrible burst into The Beano during 1944, though he had first appeared in the Adventure in 1936. Again illustrated by Watkins, countless kids followed the tales of Strang as he searched for lost cities or fabulous treasures of lost gold.

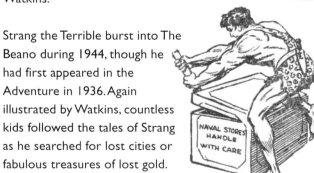

NAVAL STORES HANDLE WITH CARE

STRANG THE TERRIBLE

1 — Strang the Terrible was in search of a Lost City of which he had heard. Directly ahead of him was a grove of trees, dark and sinister. He was halfway through the grove when he sensed danger.

2 — A band of soldiers sprang from their hiding places in the branches and closed in upon Strang. A terrific struggle took place as they attempted to capture him.

3 — As Strang was led prisoner before King Agar of the Lost City he noticed a huge sword embedded in a rock. This was the sword of Thorodin, the fabled founder of the City. Strang also noticed the wolfish figure of Kark, the High Priest, standing beside the King.

4 — Strang had been weakened by the beating given him by the soldiers, but the sight of the evil-looking High Priest stirred up his defiance. King Agar gazed in awe at his magnificent strength.

5 — The soldiers slowly drew back on the command of King Agar. "Stop," he ordered. "I would have speech with this mighty stranger." The sight of Strang's amazing strength had given King Agar an idea.

6 — Later, on the balcony of his Royal Palace, Agar pointed across the square to the Scared Sword of Thorodin stood. He told how Kark had produced a parchment which demanded that the King or his champion pull the sword from the rock that very night or lose the city.

7 — Strang agreed to help Agar in his trouble and was made a guest at the Palace. This infuriated Kark, who plotted to get rid of this intruder. As Strang walked along a marble corridor Kark's priests opened a trapdoor underneath him.

8 — Strang plunged into an evil-smelling, water-filled pit and to his horror a giant crocodile with open, snapping jaws swam rapidly towards him. Kark and his priests were sure they had rid themselves of this powerful stranger.

9 — But Strang wasn't the man to be got rid of so easily. Grasping his knife, he dived deep down into the murky water and took the monster by surprise. Strang dealt it a death-blow.

10 — Meanwhile outside, the priests forced King Agar to test his strength on the scared sword. Suddenly there was a shout. It was Strang. Kark, the High Priest, turned in a fury to stop him coming to the aid of the King. How had he escaped?

11 — Pushing aside the priest, Strang slowly hauled the Sacred Sword free. Suddenly a mighty explosion rent the air. The removal of the sword had operated some hidden mechanism and the Temple of the Priests toppled and crumpled to the ground in a fiery blaze.

12 — In the eerie light of the blazing Temple, Strang stood, sword in hand. All around were the cheering people of the city, while the priests slunk away into the darkest corners they could find. They knew their reign was over.

THE war now five years behind, The Beano moved into the 50s with editor George Moonie embracing the optimistic mood of the nation. Paper shortages and their subsequent circulation capping were gone so weekly production was back – and how! On the week beginning April 22, 1950 The Beano sale was a staggering 1,974,072.

● The highest selling Beano to date April 22, 1950.

● Biffo had replaced Big Eggo on the cover in 1948.

THE 17th March 1951 is a major red and black letter day for The Beano! Dennis the Menace arrives. Billed as the world's wildest boy, Dennis was the first cartoon strip by the amazing DC Thomson staff artist David Law. Dennis would go on to become the most popular of all Beano comic strips.

LOOK! HERE'S A NEW PAL YOU'LL ENJOY—

He's the world's wildest boy!

● The first Dennis published – a black and white half-page.

25

DENNIS THE MENACE

A LITTLE SCAMP IN A VERY DULL SHIRT SMASHED MY CAR WINDOW WITH HIS BALL.

LOVE A DUCK! MUST THINK HE'S THAT YOUNG STANLEY MATTHEWS.

COULD BE HIM WITH THE LAD IN THE VERY STRIKING HOOPED JERSEY.

HUMPH! THEY'RE RIGHT—IT *IS* A VERY DULL SHIRT. TIME FOR A MENACING SCHEME.

WONDER WHEN ANYONE WILL SET FOOT ON THE MOON?

JULY 20th, 1969 WOULD BE MY GUESS. LET'S SEE IF WE CAN BEAT THAT.

CAREFUL WITH THAT POP, DENNIS.

?

GRANNY'S POP SURE IS POWERFUL STUFF.

READY TO MAKE HISTORY, TUFTY?

SHAKE!

THAT SHOULD DO THE TRICK.

-3-2-1-

FISS!

-LIFT OFF!

WHOOSH!

POP!
POP!
POP!

HAR-HAR! TUFTY WON'T NEED THIS ON THE MOON-I'LL HAVE IT.

FEELS RIGHT, SOMEHOW!

THE Dennis opposite was produced in 2001 for Dennis' 50th birthday by Beano editor Euan Kerr and long time David Law fan, artist David Parkins. It tells an entertaining tale of how Dennis got his signature red and black jersey – when, if the truth be known, he just appeared wearing the striped jersey in an early Beano cartoon.

I N 1953 and with only one text story still running, George Moonie's Beano was beginning to adopt an active, livewire cartoon style. This attracted two new art talents to the comic – Ken Reid and Leo Baxendale. The madcap drawings of the Law, Reid and Baxendale trio plus the energetic scripts from the young Beano writers produced memorable characters – Dennis the Menace, Roger the Dodger, Little Plum, Minnie the Minx, The Bash St Kids and Jonah. This new anarchic style was a landmark in British comic development.

● Minnie the Minx launches girl power!!

HE week prior to Roger appearing, an advert told readers what to expect "The World's Craftiest Dodger – Trickier than a cageful of monkeys!"

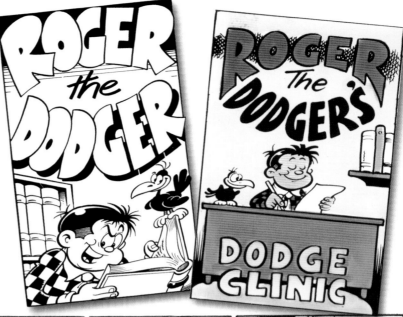

THE mayhem of the school playground outside his office window gave editor George Moonie the idea for the pupils of Bash Street School. First illustrated by Leo Baxendale, the strips were full of inventive detail and it took several readings before all the fun happenings would be spotted.

BEANO sub-editor Walter Fearn was the scriptwriter behind the unluckiest sailor in the world – Jonah.

Walter describes how he would get carried away writing a story and worry he had put too many frames on a single page for the artist Ken Reid to draw. However, when the pencil roughs came back he found that Ken had actually added more frames of his own, he so loved the arch seagoon character.

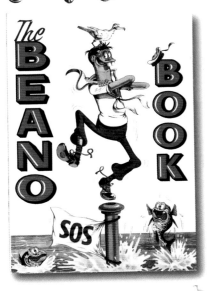

A BRAND-NEW CARGO SHIP, THE S.S. "MINERVA," IS LEAVING THE GREEK PORT OF ATHENS — BOUND FOR BRITAIN —

— ABOARD IS THE WEALTHY OWNER, FRED ARISTOTLE — BOUND FOR A GOOD DUCKING IN THE MEDITERRANEAN —

— WHILE IN HER HOLD, LIES A MASSIVE BLOCK OF MARBLE FOR SHIPMENT TO HULL — BUT BOUND FOR THE BOTTOM OF THE SEA!

THE REASON FOR THESE IMPENDING DISASTERS LIES IN THIS INNOCENT-LOOKING CRATE —

— NO! NOT THE TORTOISES — BUT THE NAUTICAL NIT-WIT WHO CRAWLED UNDERNEATH 'EM ON THE DOCK-SIDE AT ATHENS!

HO-HO! WE'RE AT SEA, MATES! THANKS FOR HIDING ME!

ALL I'VE GOT TO DO NOW, IS TO AMUSE MYSELF DOWN HERE UNTIL WE'RE TOO FAR OUT AT SEA FOR THEM TO PUT ME ASHORE AGAIN.

I. CHIPP, SCULPTOR, HULL.

AH! A BLOCK OF MARBLE.

I COULD TRY MY HAND AT SCULPTURIN'!

I'LL CARVE A STATUE OF MYSELF. THEY MIGHT PUT IT IN THE BRITISH MUSEUM.

AND SO, TO WORK —

NOT A BAD LIKENESS, EVEN ALTHOUGH I SAY IT MYSELF!

MEANWHILE, ON THE BRIDGE...

WELL, YOU CAN BE QUITE CERTAIN OF ONE THING, CAP'N! JONAH ISN'T ABOARD! I MADE A THOROUGH SEARCH.

GOOD WORK, CHARLIE!

HALF A DAY LATER

FINISHED AT LAST — AGGH!

SWAY

NO!

THE BASE IS TOO SMALL, AND AS THE SHIP ROLLS —

CRASH!

SUFFERIN' SEA-SLUGS! RIGHT THROUGH THE HULL!

HELP!

WHAT A TRAGEDY! MY STATUE WAS A WORK OF ART!

GRR-R-R! I'LL HAVE HER SALVAGED! I'LL FIND OUT WHAT HAPPENED TO HER IF IT COSTS EVERY DRACHMA I HAVE!

IT WASN'T JONAH, SIR! CHARLIE FRUIT HERE IS SURE OF THAT!

THAT'TH RIGHT, THIR! I MADE A THOROUGH THEARCH!

AND SO, AT GREAT EXPENSE, THE S.S. "MINERVA" IS RAISED FROM THE DEPTHS.

HERE SHE COMES! THE DIVERS HAVE RIVETTED A METAL PATCH OVER THE PLACE WHERE SHE WAS HOLED AND NOW THEY'RE RAISING HER WITH COMPRESSED AIR!

HOO-OO!
HISS-S-S!
S.S. MINERVA

WELL! I STILL SAY IT WASN'T JONAH, CAP'N!

YES, SIR! I CAN ALWAYS RELY ON CHARLIE TO — ERK!

MINERVA

THE PATCH!

IT WAS 'IM!

SO! YOU MADE A THOROUGH SEARCH, DID YOU, FRUIT? WELL, IN A FEW MINUTES THEY'LL BE MAKING A THOROUGH SEARCH FOR YOU, FOOL — A FRUITLESS ONE!

NO!

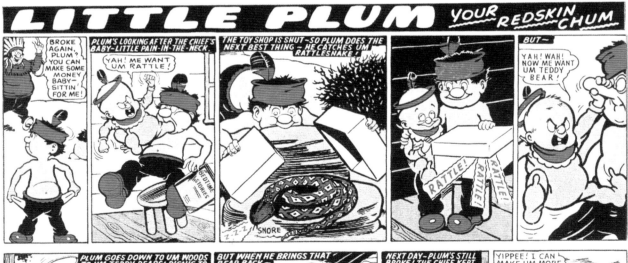

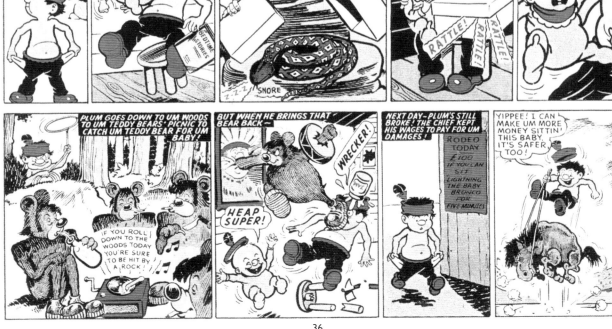

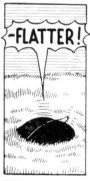

TWO big celebrations from the early sixties. Both cake guzzling covers were drawn by Dudley Watkins. In neither of the comics was there any further mention of it being a specially noteworthy issue.

A MAGICAL day in the life of Dennis – in 1968 he adopts a scruffy dog and calls him Gnasher. To the despair of adults, the authorities and peaceful suburbia this wild pair would become friends for life.

Scriptwriter Ian Gray gave artist David Law the following instructions for the design of Gnasher: 'Draw Dennis the Menace's hair, put a leg at each corner and eyes, nose and teeth at the front' - as you can see, it worked perfectly. Though scruffy, Gnasher is no mongrel, he is an Abyssinian wire-haired tripe hound.

● Dennis and Gnasher were so popular they were promoted onto the front cover during 1974.

N a 1986 storyline Gnasher goes missing. After many anxious weeks he returns, the proud father of six pups! One pup is kept – Gnipper. With his dad he forms the Gnasher and Gnipper comic strip.

- Gnasher fronts the comic in 2000.

- The most popular Beano free gifts were based upon Gnasher.

DAVE Sutherland took over the mantle of Dennis artist when ill health halted David Law in 1970. An amazingly versatile artist, Dave was already drawing Biffo the Bear and The Bash Street Kids. Each character beautifully drawn in their own individual, differing styles.

● Here he adds another pet to the Dennis and Gnasher set – Rasher! This dust-bin on legs porker would eventually get his own strip too.

MY PETS ARE ALWAYS TRYING TO OUTDO EACH OTHER!

VERY GOOD, GNASHER!

CLAP!

GRUNT! THAT'S NOTHING!

EVEN BETTER RASHER!

THAT PIG'S ALWAYS MAKING ME LOOK SMALL!

WE'RE SUBSTITUTES FOR THE GIRLS' NETBALL TEAM!

SPORTS CENTRE

WATCH ME MAKE THE SOFTIES RUN!

GNASH!

HO! HO!

I CAN MAKE THEM RUN FASTER THAN THAT!

SQUEAL! SCREAM! SHRIEK! NASTY HORRID MUD! KEEP THE GHASTLY STUFF AWAY FROM US!

BAH! HE'S MADE ME LOOK SMALL AGAIN!

HAW! HAW!

DENNIS the MENACE FAN CLUB

Attention, all Menace fans! I've started my very own fan club — and so has Gnasher! I want you all to join! There's a smashing lapel badge, and a fantastic hairy Gnasher badge, too (see below)! Details of how to join my club at foot of page.

DROP ME A LINE

Your problems answered by a famous problem child.

A £1 Postal Order will be sent to every "Beano" reader whose letter, joke or story appears on this page. Send letters to "DROP ME A LINE", using address at foot of page.

Dear Dennis, I have trouble getting up in the morning to go to school. What should I do?
Minnie the Minx.

Dear Minnie,
Your problems are over —
Don't bother getting up! Dennis.

Dear Menace,
Just a short note to let you know I think you are a jolly rotter.
Your loving enemy, Walter.

Dear Wattikins,
Why don't you join my Fan Club? All welcome — even softies.
Yours toughly, Dennis.

JOKE OF THE WEEK

QUESTION —
WHAT'S WORRIED AND LIES ON THE SEA-BED?

ANSWER ~
DENNIS'S TEACHER ON A SKIN-DIVING EXPEDITION!
(FROM ROGER THE DODGER)

GNASHER'S FANG CLUB

DEAR MENACE,
I AM BOTHERED WITH SUMS AT SCHOOL. THINGS DON'T SEEM TO ADD UP. WHAT CAN I DO? WORRIED, SMIFFY.

DEAR WORRIED, SMIFFY,
YOUR PROBLEM IS QUICKLY SOLVED — TAKE AWAY ONE PUPIL — YOURSELF, AND JOIN ME IN AN AFTERNOON'S FISHING. SEE YOU AT THE RIVER
YOURS ABSENTLY, DENNIS.

Dear Gnasher,
I want to be a howling success as a singer.
Your chum, Pug.

Dear Pug,
Why don't you join a PUP-GROUP?
Your faithful pal, Gnasher.

BNO. 5.6.76

HAIRY BADGE with MOVING EYES

Dear Gnasher,
I have a giraffe as a pet, but I don't have enough room for him.
Worried, Grandpa.

Dear Grandpa, My advice is to go and live in a lighthouse. Your faithful pal, Gnasher.

Send me a story about your pet!

NAME _____

ADDRESS _____

_____

_____

I enclose a 30p Postal Order

To join the "Dennis the Menace Fan Club" (including "Gnasher's Fang Club") fill in the coupon opposite and send it to:-

DENNIS THE MENACE FAN CLUB,
P.O. BOX 66,
DUNDEE, DD1 9LN.

In addition to the 2 badges you will receive a membership card, club secrets and a smart club wallet.

T HE Beano start the Dennis the Menace Fan Club (incorporating Gnasher's Fang Club) in 1976. It is instantly popular and membership requests come flooding in. A few years later there are over 1,000,000 members.

THESE HAIRY BADGES FROM YOUR "FANG" CLUB SHOULD GIVE US LOADS OF FUN, GNASHER!

GNESH!

HEH! HEH! THIS SHOULD BE GOOD FOR A LAUGH!

● The hairy Gnasher badge with moving eyes is the most popular part of the membership pack.

Dear "Beano" Reader,
You are now a member of my Fan Club, and here's your membership card to prove it! Fill in the details and keep the card safely in the special wallet.
Remember - always wear your club badges.
All the best,
Dennis.

P.S. GRUNT-GNASH-YOWL-SNUFFLE! (That's Gnasher saying "Welcome to my Fang Club, too!")
P.P.S. Club secrets overleaf.

PASSWORDS

TOP SECRET

Members should greet each other like this:-

D.I.N.G!*

D.O.N.G!**

* Stands for "Dennis Is Never Good!"
** "Dennis Owns Naughty Gnasher!"

GNASHWORDS

Secretly supplied by Gnasher — for use only by Fang Club Members.

GNOSH! Dinner's ready.   GNASHTY! Dinner's horrible.

GNARK-GNARK! My big sister's always going on at me.

GNOTT GNOTTY- I'm well-behaved.

GNOTT GNICE- I'm not well-behaved.

GNIGHT-GNIGHT — Sleep well.

Member of the "Dennis the Menace Fan Club."

NAME_____

ADDRESS_____

_____

STICK A PHOTO OF YOURSELF HERE.

DATE

Also a member of "Gnasher's Fang Club."

● Dennis speaks to his fan club from the pages of The Beano.
'Your problems answered by a famous problem child'.

● Members are given secret passwords

PICTURE strip adventure stories played a big part in the Beano success story. They were a main feature of the comic from the earliest days to the mid-seventies. These examples were all huge favourites in their time.

DANNY WESTON and his dolphins have succeeded in damaging the pirate submarine "Red Shark" which is under the command of the sinister Captain Bruno. The boy has trailed the crippled pirate craft to its base—a huge, flooded cavern inside the volcanic island of Balapos. Then Flash, Danny's favourite dolphin, accidentally sets off an alarm system in the cavern. Immediately a steel portcullis drops across the entrance, cutting off Danny's escape . . .

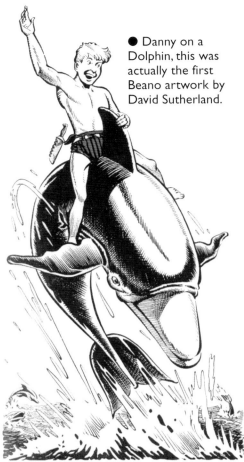

● Danny on a Dolphin, this was actually the first Beano artwork by David Sutherland.

● The incredible mechanical swordfish invented by Professor Gray and piloted by his son, another Danny.

● A rip-roaring all action swashbuckler! The Laughing Pirate plagued the Spanish and Portuguese galleons. Interestingly, it was illustrated by Portuguese artist Vitor Peon.

A STIRRING tale of Sir Hugo Merriman, the boldest buccaneer ever to sail the Spanish Main. Sir Hugo's answer to every danger is a burst of defiant laughter, and the Spaniards, for many years his mortal enemies, have given him the nickname of the Laughing Pirate.

● Red Rory of the Eagles. The young Jacobite hero fought his highland cause for many years, appearing in 13 series of the story.

RED RORY OF THE EAGLES

● Honestly, these bikes were state of the art in 1963.

● What boy did *not* want his own remote control army after reading a General Jumbo tale?

ATTEN-SHUN!   PRE-SENT ARMS!   HERE COMES —

GENERAL JUMBO

HE last young hero! Billy the Cat was the last new adventure strip character to appear in The Beano. This is his debut from 1967.

The amazing adventures of

BILLY the CAT

CATCH HIM IF YOU CAN !

STARTING NOW!

All at once the ball was kicked out of play to land at William's feet . . .

HURRY UP, WILLIAM—KICK IT BACK!

COME ON, CHUM!

At Burnham Academy sports field, a quiet, bespectacled schoolboy was watching his school team playing Kingsley College. His name was William Grange, and he had joined the Academy a few weeks before.

After the match, William strolled off to his home in one of Burnham's new housing estates. The house was owned by his Aunt Mabel, with whom William had lived ever since his parents were killed in a road crash. William had just started his supper when . . .

..IT HAS JUST BEEN ANNOUNCED THAT £10,000 WORTH OF WATCHES AND JEWELLERY HAVE BEEN STOLEN FROM HENDRICK'S SHOP IN BURNHAM HIGH STREET..

HAW! HAW! HE'S MISSED IT COMPLETELY! YOU'LL NEVER WIN ANY SPORTS PRIZES, WILLIAM!

William smiled to himself as one of his school chums tapped the ball back on to the pitch.

Not long afterwards . . .

I'M OFF TO MY ROOM, AUNT MABEL.

Meanwhile, in the High Street, police detectives were still busy at Hendrick's shop.

HENDRICK'S

POLICE

Suddenly—

GOSH! LOOK AT THAT!

POL

The black leather-suited figure dropped lightly to the street . . .

HEY!

. . . and stooped to pick up something from the road. As the policemen closed in he darted off again and shinned quickly up a drainpipe with dazzling speed.

HOI! COME BACK!

WHAT AN ATHLETE! I'VE NEVER SEEN ANYTHING LIKE IT!

Like a huge cat, the black figure leapt away over the rooftops. Once out of sight of the police, he looked at the object he had picked up in the street. It was a book of matches on which was printed "The Grand Hotel, Burnham." Faintly pencilled inside were the figures 201.

This was the tallest building in Burnham, and soon the cat-like figure was scampering up its sheer walls.

He reached a certain window on the sixth floor . . .

THIS SHOULD BE ROOM 201...AH!

Silently he un-wound a weighted rope from his waist and then sprang into action—

AARGH!

The third crook tried to make a get-away, but again the weighted rope snaked outwards....

The thieves were going to be sorry that one of them had accidentally dropped the book of matches.

Snatching up the suitcase containing the watches and jewellery, the cat-like figure climbed out of the window and slithered quickly down to the canopy over the hotel entrance. A few minutes later . . .

AH! A POLICE-CAR ON PATROL.

THERE YOU ARE, OFFICER —WITH THE COMPLIMENTS OF BILLY THE CAT!

THIEVES ARE IN ROOM 201 GRAND HOTEL

BE SEEING YOU!

HEY! WAIT A MINUTE!

Not long afterwards, Billy the Cat was climbing into Mabel Grange's house . . .

Inside a bedroom he quickly removed his strange head-dress —to reveal the features of William Grange!

A few minutes later—

DON'T BE LONG, WILLIAM. A YOUNG FELLOW LIKE YOU NEEDS HIS SLEEP.

OK, AUNT MABEL. I'VE NEARLY FINISHED.

MORE ABOUT *BILLY THE CAT* NEXT WEEK!

●1980 and it's Dennis the footballer

AS 1980 dawned and other interests grabbed the attention of children, the sales of the weekly comics began to slip. The sales of annuals held up and in most cases actually increased. These iconic books are still eagerly awaited in the run up to Christmas every year.

The Beano Book covers normally had a before and after theme, with Dennis featuring in every one of them. Some were surreal and occasionally, bizarre.

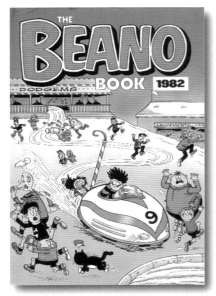

● All the fun of the fair in 1982

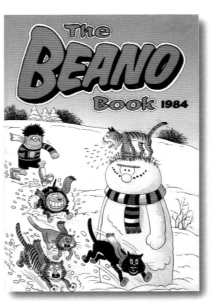

● Winter blunderland in 1984

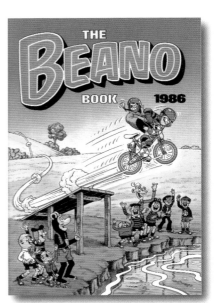

● Daredevil Dennis in 1986

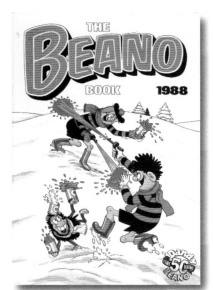

● Dennis and his female counterpart, Minnie, in 1988

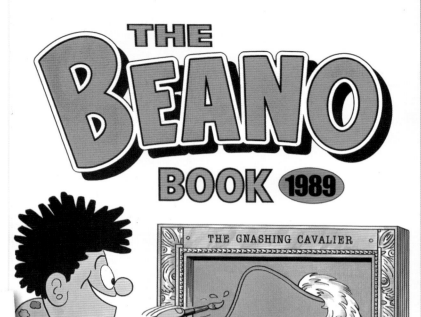

THE GNASHING CAVALIER

● A surreal cover for book number 50 in 1989

● 1994 saw a different style of cover

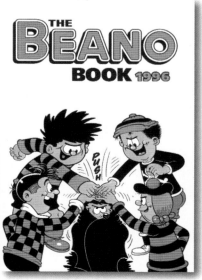

● Back to normal by 1996

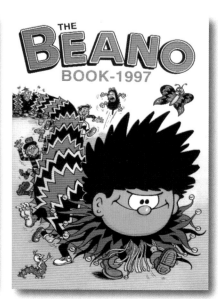

● Dennis-Gnasher conga in 1997

EVERY year summers, yes, even British ones, are made brighter for comic fans by the Beano Summer Special. The appearance of this colourful mega-comic heralds the coming holiday season, a tradition now going back 35 years.

The Beano scriptwriters love working on the Summer Special as it gives them an opportunity to take their storylines to holiday destinations, the more bizarre the better. Photo spreads, features and puzzles all add to the happy atmosphere of this mag.

The first Summer Special came out in 1963 and was a rare joint publication between The Dandy and The Beano.

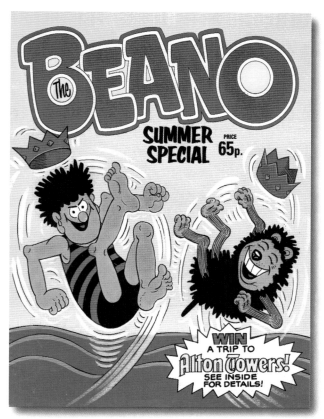

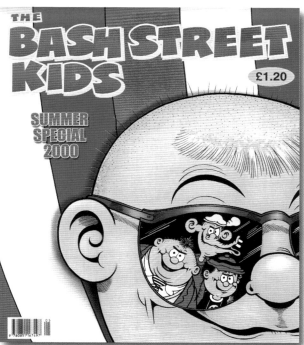

● The young girl model in this Alice in Beanoland story is Donna Air who would go on to be a celeb TV presenter.

● The Bash St Kids landed their own Summer Special, a celebration of school holidays.

SINCE the first issue The Beano had always had strips about the most colourful of characters. However, it was not until 1993 that they would all appear colourful.

● Dennis uses colour in his usual fashion.

● Full colour printing of every page gave the characters more life. Roger the Dodger pages had been two colour, red and black, now he could blush if a dodge went wrong.

● The first ever colour version of the world's speediest kid: Billy Whizz!

HE Beano survived the millennium bug and early in the new 21st century there was two special issues. Beano 3000 in January 2000 and Dennis the Menace's 50th birthday issue in March 2001.

DENNIS the Menace 50th birthday was marked by a special comic plus his own sticker collection and album. Later in the year a commerative book would be published.

● Dennis parties! How else would a Dennis party turn out?

● Chris Evans rocks with Dennis and the Dinmakers to mark 3000 Beanos.

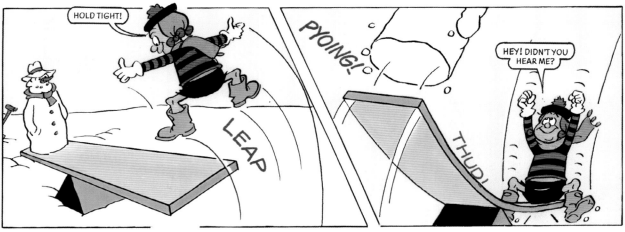

THIS Minnie the Minx was the 2000th weekly episode drawn by artist Jim Petrie (he portrayed himself quite accurately in the story). It appeared in the Beano in Jan 13th 2001. Jim had first drawn Minnie in 1961, taking over from the original artist Leo Baxendale and this figure does not take into count the numerous Minnie stories he drew for Beano Annuals and Specials. A truly awesome total.

BEANOMAX was launched in February 2007 as a monthly Big Brother to the classic Beano Weekly. Aimed at the 8–13 age group, the content is made up of long comic strips featuring Beano favourites and life-style features — puzzles, amazing facts, reviews, interviews, etc. Though Dennis the Menace took star billing initially, a new, eponymous character, Max was introduced as front man in Spring 2007. Drawn in a new, computer-based style by staff artist Jim Dewar, Max takes everything to the ultimate.

The Beano today provides the sharpest entertainment for kids but this cult comic classic is really for fun people of all ages. The editorial and artists continually create new characters – these examples being among the most recent.

● Johnny Bean, illustrator Laura Howell, oddly enough, the first female artist to land a regular strip in The Beano.

● Ratz, illustrated by Hunt Emerson, already has a strong following.

● These sketches suggest that Dennis and Gnasher's updated tree house will be rather special.

FIRST look at development work on the 'fang'tastic new Dennis and Gnasher animated series. The series is scheduled to premiere on BBC in 2009.
This will be the third series for the Beano pair.

● Bedroom of a menace

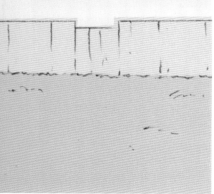

The Beano Family Album

● 1938 the first Beano staff. Seated is 24 year old editor, George Moonie.

● 1955 Paper store at the Manchester print works, some of this paper would become Beanos. Each reel of paper is approx 5 miles long.

● 1969 The Mayor of Salford enjoys The Beano on a visit to the printing works in Manchester.

● 1960 Loading copies at Manchester depot despatch.

● 1985 Prime Minister Margaret Thatcher visits The Beano office. With her is ex chief-sub Walter Fearn(left) and now managing editor George Moonie.

Printed and Published in Great Britain by D.C.Thomson & Co., Ltd. 185 Fleet Street, London, EC 4A 2HS